the # BAD GUYS

EPISODE

6

ALIEN vs
BAD GUYS

FIRST PUBLISHED BY SCHOLASTIC PRESS,
A DIVISION OF SCHOLASTIC AUSTRALIA PTY LIMITED IN 2018.
TEXT AND ILLUSTRATIONS COPYRIGHT © AARON BLABEY, 2018.

PUBLISHED BY SCHOLASTIC SINGAPORE, OPERATING UNDER
GROLIER INTERNATIONAL INC., 81 UBI AVENUE 4, #02-30 UB. ONE,
SINGAPORE 408830. GROLIER INTERNATIONAL INC. IS A SUBSIDIARY
OF SCHOLASTIC INC., NEW YORK, 10012 (USA).

THIS EDITION PUBLISHED UNDER LICENSE FROM SCHOLASTIC AUSTRALIA PTY LIMITED.

ISBN 978-981-47-7682-0

TYPESET IN JANSON, ELO, KERBEROS FANG AND BEHANCE.
DESIGN BY NICOLE STOFBERG.

FIRST PRINTING, MAY 2018

REPRINTED ON JANUARY 2019 IN MALAYSIA

GOOD GUYS CLUB SAVES THE WORLD!

There are celebrations across the globe tonight, as the evil **DR RUPERT MARMALADE** has been **DEFEATED!**

TIFFANY FLUFFIT 6

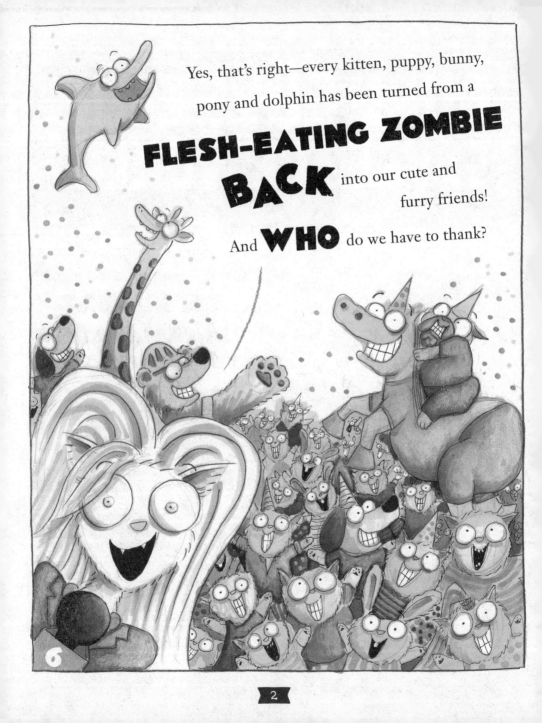

Yes, that's right—every kitten, puppy, bunny, pony and dolphin has been turned from a

FLESH-EATING ZOMBIE BACK into our cute and furry friends!

And **WHO** do we have to thank?

THE GOOD GUYS CLUB!

AS GOOD AS IT GETS!

Sure, the name might be lame, but I doubt there's a creature on this planet that wouldn't like to give those

CHEEKY, WHOLESOME BOYS
a hug!

The **LOVABLE**
Mr Wolf!

The **BRILLIANT**
Mr Snake!

The **POWERFUL**
Mr Shark!

And
THE OTHER ONE
that is some kind of fish.
Possibly a sardine.

They are the **GREATEST LEGENDS OF OUR TIME!**

ARTIST'S IMPRESSION

And I'd personally like to add that I **ALWAYS** thought they were awesome.

I really did . . .

So let's send them all a great, big . . .

THANK YOU,

wherever they may be!

To the gang that saved
the world—

NOT BAD, GUYS ...

not bad at all!

It's nice to think of you out there ...

wherever you are . . .

protecting us . . .

you GREAT, BIG, BEAUTIFUL, TOUGH GUYS . . .

CHAPTER 1

DEEP SPACE, DEEP POO

I think I'm
going to cry . . .

Me too . . .

I'm already crying . . .

I can't *stop* crying!
I'm SO SCARED!

And we're trapped inside its
space station on the moon
**WITHOUT A
ROCKET.**

So **HOW ARE WE
GOING TO GET
OUT OF HERE?!**

Shhh! It'll hear us!
What are we going to
do? We can't hide
here forever . . .

SPLODGE!

Eeeeee!
Nobody
move . . .

Oh man, this is SO not fair.
We've come so far!
Finally, everyone thinks we're
heroes! We can't die here.
We need a plan . . .

Hey! What's *that*?

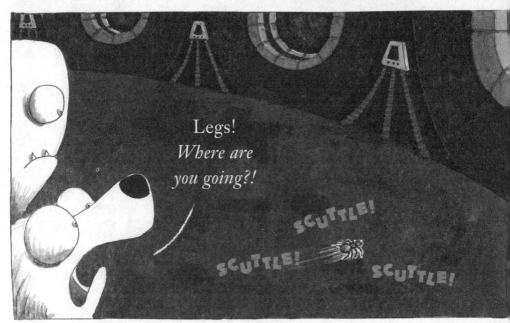

Legs!
*Where are
you going?!*

Is it the little room where we all die?

But this is an

ALIEN SPACESHIP!

How will you even know how to work it?

How hard can it be? I bet there are a whole **BUNCH OF LANGUAGES** on here and probably some from **EARTH** and . . . yep . . . and what if I just punch in a few **CO-ORDINATES** and . . . yep . . .

ready to launch

destination > earth

I'd say we're good to go!

Man, you just **HACKED AN ALIEN COMPUTER!** Seriously, we don't give you as much credit as you deserve. Let's hear it for Legs, guys!

OK, I'll tell you what— why don't you stay here and **HAVE A PARADE FOR LEGS** and I'll see you back on Earth. OK?

You are the rudest little—

In fact, how's it going out there, little buddy?

Legs? Is everything cool?

LEGS?!

· CHAPTER 2 ·
AND THEN THERE WERE FOUR

LEGS?!

Oh no, this isn't good at all . . .

Where is he?!

Hey, you know what?

The ole Escape Pod is all

GOOD TO GO

so I say we just jump right back in and skedaddle, whaddya say?

Are you serious?

YEAH!

I mean, there's **PLENTY** of these pod things. Legs can just take the **NEXT ONE**.

He's probably just gone to

GRAB A SANDWICH

or something and I'm sure he wouldn't mind if we took off and met him back on—

NO-ONE LEAVES UNTIL WE FIND LEGS. GOT IT?

I mean, yeah, we **COULD** do that, but don't you think it makes more sense to—

WHAT ARE YOU TALKING ABOUT?!

LEGS IS OUR **FRIEND!**

HE'S THE **ONLY REASON** WE KNOW ABOUT THE ESCAPE PODS

IN THE FIRST PLACE AND **YOU WANT TO LEAVE HIM BEHIND?!**

Hey, Piranha! Keep it down!

NO! I'VE HAD IT UP TO HERE WITH THIS ROTTEN LITTLE DIABLO!

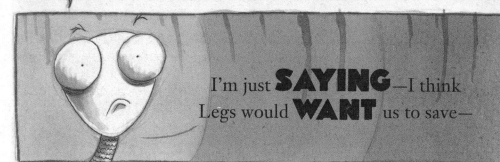

I'm just **SAYING**—I think
Legs would **WANT** us to save—

YOU ARE THE MOST SELFISH . . .

Piranha!

 MEAN-HEARTED . . .

 Really, man—*shoosh!*

 SON OF A WORM I'VE EVER . . .

Is it just me,
or do I have an

ALIEN BUTT

pointed at my face?

Piranha! *Look out!*

Oh my stars!
It uses its
BUTTS AS HANDS!

PIRANHA!

That's it, I'm out of here.

Last one to the Escape Pod is an alien's brunch . . .

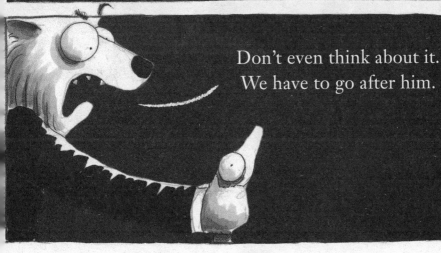

Don't even think about it. We have to go after him.

What **ARE YOU SAYING?!**
That thing has **BUTT HANDS!**
You really want to go looking for a creature with
great, big **POOPY**

BUTT HANDS?!

Shut up and listen!

TOOOOOOOOOO MAANNNYYYYYY

BUUUUTTTTTTSSSSSSSSSSS!!!

He's still ALIVE!
We can follow his voice!

Let's go!

But what about the Escape Pod?
Maybe I should just stay here
and look after it, in case . . .

· CHAPTER 3 ·
THE LADY ALIEN

Yeah. Can I just point out that we seem to be entering an even creepier part of an already

INSANELY CREEPY SPACESHIP!

I, for one, strongly vote against this.

You want to vote?

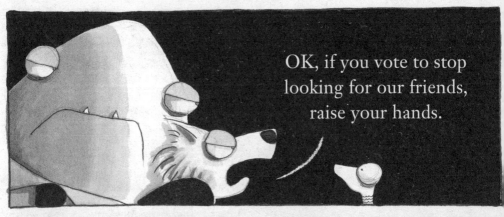

OK, if you vote to stop looking for our friends, raise your hands.

No hands? OK then,
LET'S KEEP LOOKING!

Oh, you're hilarious.
I hope the alien takes
you next.

You should be
so lucky—

AAAAARRRGH!
IT'S GOT
ME!

Oh really? And you're trained in using **BIZARRE ALIEN WEAPONS**, are you?

No, but maybe we could figure it out.

FIGURE IT OUT?!
OK, well why don't you take a few minutes to learn how to

SPEAK ALIEN

and then—have a flick through the

INSTRUCTION MANUALS

and then—mosey on over and TEACH US how to use them too! Yeah. GREAT idea. Let's just all take a seat and

FIGURE IT OUT!

No! Snake!

Don't interrupt me, man!
You need to hear this—

SNAKE!
IT'S HERE!
AARRGGHHH!!!

SHARK?!
Man, you are SO
good at disguises.

I know.

But how did you manage
to make this so quickly?

I'm just good at it.
Let it go.

What's with the **DRESS?!**

I'm going to pretend to be a **LADY ALIEN**. And when the **MARMALADE ALIEN** tries to make friends with me, I'll get him to show us where he keeps the creatures that he's captured and **BINGO—** we can rescue the guys. **THAT'S** the plan.

OK, your costumes may have worked in the past, but what you just said is so stupid it makes me want to eat my own face.

Well, I like it.

IT'S INSANE!

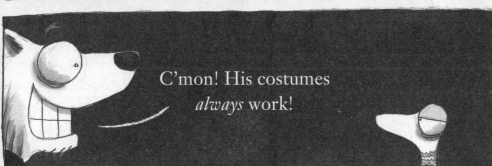

C'mon! His costumes *always* work!

Yeah, but this time he's pretending to be a LADY ALIEN and

HE DOESN'T EVEN KNOW WHAT A LADY ALIEN LOOKS LIKE!

That's a chance I'm willing to take.

CHAPTER 4

ROUND IN CIRCLES

It's so dark.
Why is it so dark?
It seems to be
getting darker . . .
Don't you think it's
REALLY dark?

YES! WELL SPOTTED! IT'S DARK!
WHAT DO YOU WANT?
A *COOKIE?*
OBVIOUSLY, IT'S DARK.

Give me a break!
I'm **TERRIFIED**!
Everyone's gone. Even Shark!
But we can't give up! If we just
keep searching I **KNOW**
we'll find them. We're getting
CLOSE, I can feel it.

Oh really? We're getting *close*?
Then how do you explain **THIS** . . .

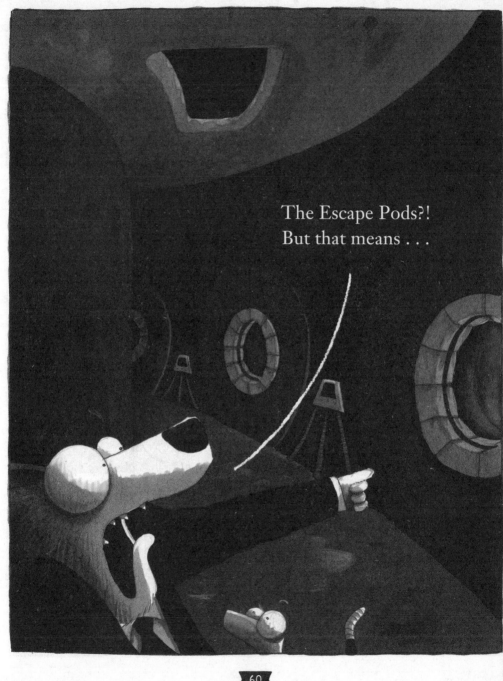

The Escape Pods?!
But that means . . .

It **MEANS** we've been **WALKING AROUND IN CIRCLES**.

Listen to me, Wolf . . .

I'll admit it, **PART OF ME** really does want to be a hero. It's true. Part of me really, *really* does. But you know what I've learnt from following you around on all these stupid missions? Do you know what I've learnt from every ridiculous situation you've put us in?

DO YOU?

I've learnt I'm *not* a hero.
I know you want me to be one . . .

But I'm really, really not.

I know **YOU** want to be a hero.
And who knows—

MAYBE YOU ARE.

But I also think that you're **CRAZY**.

And I think, one day, you'll make

just one too many stupid decisions

and you **WILL** go and get

yourself eaten by an alien.

And Wolf?

I think that day is today.

I've never had a friend before, Wolf. And even though I do call you an idiot quite a lot . . .
I know that you're the best friend I'll ever have. And I don't want to lose you. So . . .

Please get in the Escape Pod with me.

You know I can't, Mr Snake.

And you know why, too.

I can't **MAKE** you do anything, buddy. What you do next is up to you. There's the **ESCAPE POD**. If you really want to leave, then go ahead, get in and go. But I have a feeling that you'll do the right—

WHAT?!
I didn't think you'd
actually get in!

Why? Because of my little
speech? Well yeah, I meant it
and everything but there's an

**ALIEN WITH
BUTT-HANDS**

out there so basically,

ALL BETS ARE OFF

and—

What?

• CHAPTER 5 •
THE PIT OF DOOM

Wha . . . ?

I can't move!

Yeah, it's **DRIED SNOT**.
It came out of the alien's nose holes.

Shark!

Well, considering how
many butts it has, I
suppose we should be
grateful it's just snot.

Legs!

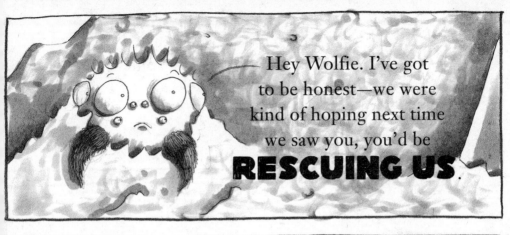

Hey Wolfie. I've got to be honest—we were kind of hoping next time we saw you, you'd be **RESCUING US**.

It's true. We're pleased to see you, but I think we're all pretty disappointed, too.

Yep. I don't know what else to say.

Don't worry, guys! I think you're
forgetting something . . .

Mr Snake!

Is that meant to be funny?

No! I believe in him the way I believe in **ALL OF YOU!**

I'm kind of offended by that, hermano.

C'mon guys! I bet he's coming up with a plan to save us **RIGHT NOW!**

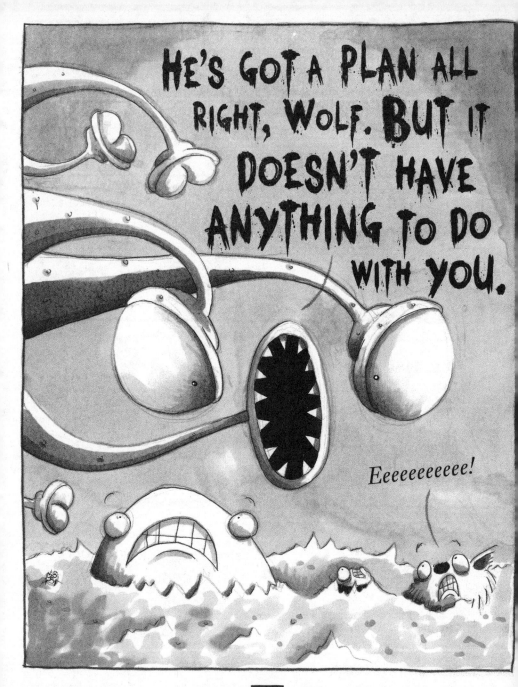

LET ME SHOW YOU...

What a surprise.

Yeah. What a shocker.

I can't believe he left us . . .

REALLY?! YOU ACTUALLY CAN'T BELIEVE IT?!

79

CHAPTER 6

THE END OF THE ROAD

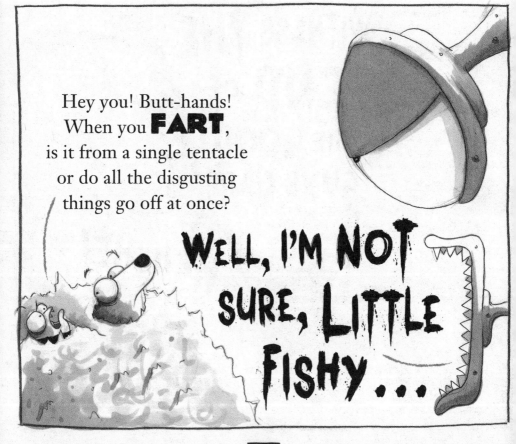

Hey you! Butt-hands! When you **FART**, is it from a single tentacle or do all the disgusting things go off at once?

WELL, I'M NOT SURE, LITTLE FISHY....

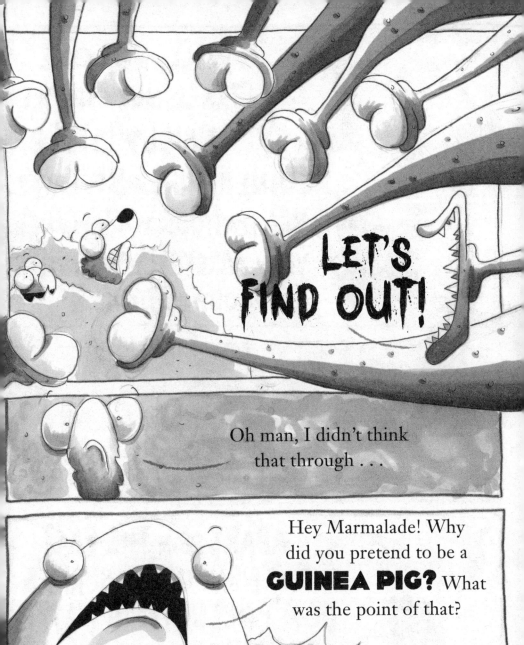

LET'S FIND OUT!

Oh man, I didn't think that through . . .

Hey Marmalade! Why did you pretend to be a **GUINEA PIG?** What was the point of that?

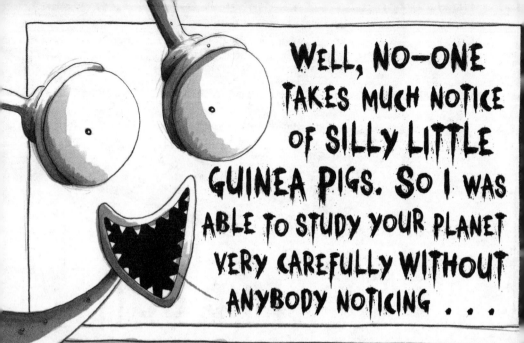

WELL, NO—ONE TAKES MUCH NOTICE OF SILLY LITTLE GUINEA PIGS. SO I WAS ABLE TO STUDY YOUR PLANET VERY CAREFULLY WITHOUT ANYBODY NOTICING . . .

And what did you learn?

APART FROM THE FACT THAT PIRANHAS AND SHARKS DON'T NEED TO BE IN WATER AS MUCH AS YOU'D THINK?

Yeah. Apart from that . . .

I LEARNT THAT YOUR PLANET IS HELPLESS.

AND IT WILL BE MINE.

I feel so stupid. I thought you were doing all of this just because you didn't like being **CUTE** and **CUDDLY**.

Oh, that wasn't a lie.
On my planet, **I AM** cute and cuddly.
And **I HATE** it. Don't get me started.

Is your name even 'Marmalade'?

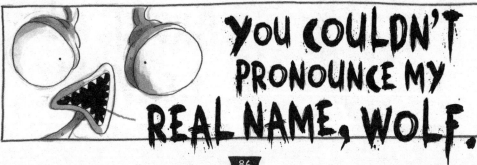

YOU COULDN'T PRONOUNCE MY REAL NAME, WOLF.

Yeah, yeah. That sounds great, KDJFdddd— whatever, and yeah, we all saw your weird, creepy **WEAPONS**, but you know what? You don't stand a chance!

OH REALLY? AND WHY'S THAT?

Because there's only **ONE** of you and you're no match for **AGENT FOX** and the **INTERNATIONAL LEAGUE OF HEROES!**

HMMM. THAT FOX IS VERY CLEVER...

BUT, GUESS WHAT?

IT'S NOT JUST ME! THERE ARE THOUSANDS OF US . . . .

Oh no.

· CHAPTER 7 ·
PICK ON SOMEONE YOUR OWN SIZE

Bring it, guinea pig.

You did it, Snake!

YOU CAME BACK!

YOU CAME BACK!

What changed your mind?

I guess I just finally got sick of being a Bad Guy.

Hey Chicos! As much as I want to dance my dance of joy right now, there's a whole **ALIEN ARMY OUT THERE WAITING TO DESTROY EARTH!**

We need to get home and warn **AGENT FOX.**

It's **KDJFLOER HGCOINWERU HCGLEIRWFHEK LWJFHXALHW!**

But how?!

MY SPECIES CAN HOLD OUR BREATH IN SPACE FOR UP TO NINE WEEKS, IF WE HAVE TO. SO I JUST FLOATED AROUND TO THE BACK DOOR . . .

AND MY **FRIENDS** LET ME **BACK IN.**

Wait a minute!

· CHAPTER 8 ·
THE POD

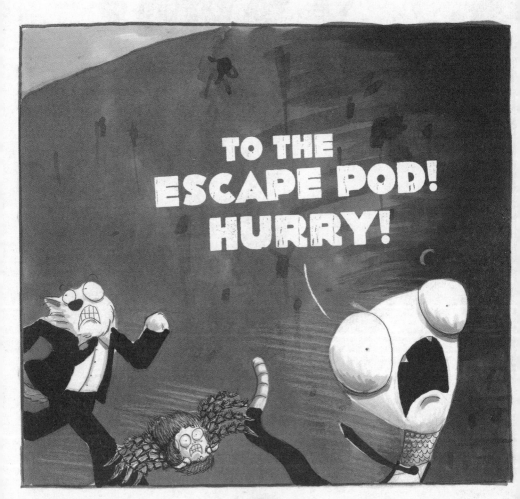

TO THE
ESCAPE POD!
HURRY!

I'm sorry, Legs, I had to fire off the first Pod to **TRICK** Marmalade. How long will it take you to prep another one?

I'll do it as fast as I can, Mr Hero!

Snake, I'm so proud of you! I mean . . . *how did you get that weapon thing to work?!*

I just . . . figured it out.

SNAP!

EEEEEE! Oh man, they're everywhere!

Watch out!

Legs, I hate to rush
you but—

I'm on it . . .

I don't mind rushing you!

HURRY
CHICO!

I'm on it!

Everyone get in!

Um . . .

Um *WHAT*?!

There's a setting here that kind of bothers me. I'm not sure what it means.

WHO CARES WHAT IT MEANS?!

JUST GET IN HERE AND SEND US BACK TO EARTH!

Yeah . . . OK . . . I guess it'll be OK . . .

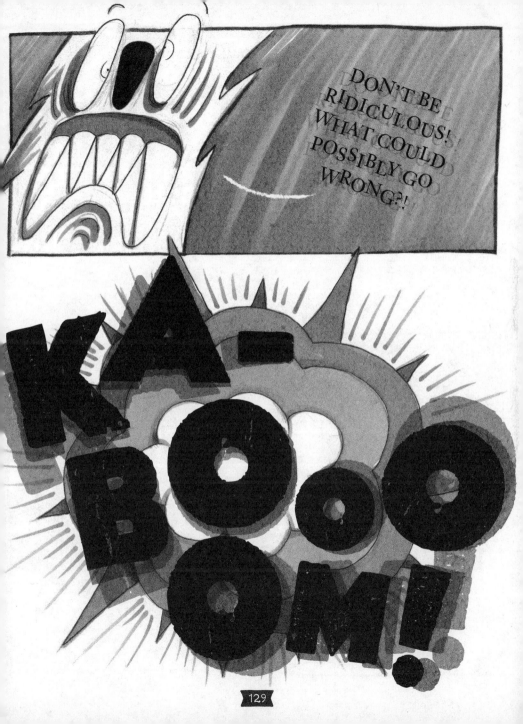

· CHAPTER 9 ·

OUT OF THE FRYING PAN, INTO THE....

HANG ON, THAT'S NOT INVENTED YET...

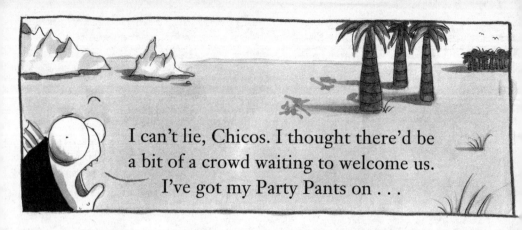

I can't lie, Chicos. I thought there'd be a bit of a crowd waiting to welcome us. I've got my Party Pants on . . .

Yeah. And we have to warn Agent Fox.

Where is everyone?

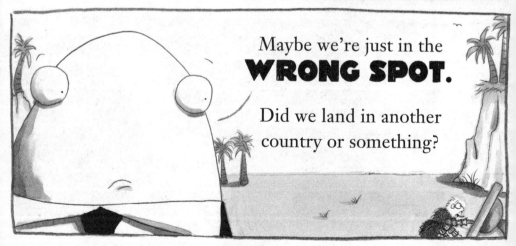

Maybe we're just in the **WRONG SPOT.**

Did we land in another country or something?

Ahhhh, no. As far as I can tell, we've landed right back where we arranged to **MEET AGENT FOX.**

What do you mean, Legs? We're in the **MIDDLE OF NOWHERE**. You must be reading that thing wrong.

Hmmm. I wish I was . . .

Don't stress, guys! We're home! That's the main thing. We're home, but this time it's *different*. This time we're **HEROES!**

Ohhhhh. Being heroes isn't the only thing that's different . . .

What do you mean, Legs?

Well, remember that setting that was bothering me? It seems . . . it was the control for a slightly

DIFFERENT KIND OF TRAVEL . . .

You mean that's the thing that made us go so **FAST?**

Well, maybe . . . but that's not what I mean . . .

Spit it out, Spider! **WHERE ARE WE?!**

Mr Snake, the question isn't **'WHERE'**. . .

65 MILLION BC?! Are you kidding?! **65 MILLION BC?!** But that's when . . .

When what?

Oh my stars! You're right! That's when there were . . .

That's when there were

WHAT?!

DINOS

TO BE CONTINUED . . .

IT'S ON.

EPISODE 7
COMING SOON!